Where's Zebulon

A Book of Poetry and Short Stories

Amuna Yisrael

ROYSTON
Publishing

BK Royston Publishing
P. O. Box 4321
Jeffersonville, IN 47131
502-802-5385
http://www.bkroystonpublishing.com
bkroystonpublishing@gmail.com

Cover Design: Elite Cover Designs

ISBN-13: 978-1-955063-76-0

Printed in the United States of America

Dedication

This book is dedicated to my family and friends who through the years have showed up willing to listen to me share my gift, and who are waiting to read my first book as a published writer!

I love you, and you know who you are.

Table of Contents

Introduction

Zebulon, Georgia, is located sixty-five miles southeast of Atlanta. "Where's Zebulon, A Book of Poetry and Short Stories," is a portrayal of my early life through my life to date. In the Hebrew language, Zebulon means 'dwelling of honor.' It is the name of the sixth son of the Old Testament Jacob, father of the Twelve Lost Tribes of Israel, and his first wife, Leah. I like to think Zebulon, Georgia, is named in honor of Jacob's sixth son, but unfortunately, it was not. However, it is the place where my great grandparents were born into slavery and where I, over one hundred years later, first exercised my civil rights. As a little girl, Zebulon is where I witnessed secrets I shouldn't have had to witness. It's the place I was forced to leave in shame when my parents' marriage ended. It's where my family split up and never came back together. It's the place I'll continue to return to because it keeps me believing in myself.

Zebulon represents my strength, my worth. It makes me who I am. Zebulon is my hometown.

My Journey

My journey had allowed me to survive times in my life when a slow and deliberate attack on my always-broken heart, had invaded my happiness. Those times methodically tore away my protectiveness and left my emotions raw and exposed. I was feeling that cut-to-the-quick pain. My fifty-three-year-old pain had crossed paths and formed a bond with the memory of my seven-year-old pain.

To escape a mental prison that held me captive and unable to figure out my own story, I sought inner peace by writing. After spending forty years in a wilderness created by others who misused my goodness, I discovered 'my' voice. Writing about my pain and shame has freed me. Now I realize no one beat me to it, and I'm the only one chosen to be me, but I had been choosing not to be myself. I had been chasing after dreams but stuck on habits that kept my pace at a slow crawl. I had been grasping for my dreams but could never reach out and touch them because I was dreaming my dreams through someone else's experiences.

Today I represent one of many survivors recovering from some form of mental and/or physical captivity. Those survivors who've had their voices ignored, their intelligence denied, and their emotions pimped. And these are my psalms...

I Am a Poet

I am a Poet!
I am a Writer!
I am an Author!
I am a Storyteller!

Me!

Scorned by some
Mourned by others
But blessed beyond my control!

Avenged by ancestors who, in god-like fashion,
stood in the way of weapons formed against me that
did not prosper. Having themselves passed this way
before, this particular path they prepared for me.
Because of them, I breathe the breath of freedom in
each of my next breaths. Face my next foe. Win
my next chance to be, to continue to exist and
'know' who I am.

Me!

As I am this day!

Writing myself out of the darkness and into the
light, and into the real truth that...

I am a Storyteller!
I am an Author!
I am a Writer!
I am a Poet!

Seven...Again

Mama, you goin' up the country...again?
You leavin' me...again?

I promise to be a good girl...if you stay.
If it's something 'I' did to run you away.
Is there something I can say?
To make you stay?

Last time I missed you so much.
Will you miss 'me' this time?
Last time you didn't say.

You see, I have this hole right here, inside my heart.
And it feels heavy to me.
Only you can make it go away..
Will you?
Please?

Do you hear me talkin'?
Do you see me sittin' at the foot of your bed?
Have 'you' ever watched 'me' sleepin'?
Seen my teary eyes
Peepin' at 'cha?

Is it my bad luck from breaking that mirror?
That keeps you from staying here...
With me?
I'm so tired of tasting tears,
So, will you hold me and taste mine for me?
Are your tears salty, too?

Don't you care how much I need you?
I know I need to be a big girl,
But it's harder when you're not here.
Did Big Mama ever leave you behind?
A number of times?

When you leave me, people can tell you're gone
Just by lookin' at me.
I hate it when they know you're gone,
And I hate it even more that I can't hide it.

You don't know when you'll be back?
Don't want another fight,
So, I better not ask Daddy, right?

I need to hear you say I mean the world to you.
I need to hear you say,
'Ok, I'll stay and never, ever leave you again.'
Please say it!
Today?

I Taught Daddy to Write His Name

On a hot day in Zebulon, Georgia, in the early summer of 1961, Daddy rounded the corner of our house in his bluish-gray 1952 Plymouth. He pulled up to the end of the driveway and stopped. With braids flapping and bare feet covered in red dust, I went racing to greet him. Just as Daddy stepped out of his car, I wrapped myself around his legs, hugging him. He asked what I'd been doing all day, but before I could answer, he asked if I could write his name on a piece of paper for him. Just four years old and learning to print my own name, I said, "okay." We went inside the house. I grabbed a pencil and tore out a piece of that manila tablet paper with thick lines. I sat down at the kitchen table and wrote Daddy's name ever so carefully on that top red line: *Jim Henry Grier.* I handed the paper to Daddy, and he gently tore off his name, folded it, and put it in his wallet.

The following week on Daddy's payday, my sister and I went to town with him to Mr. Wade's Grocery Store, where he always cashed his checks. Up until then, I'd seen Daddy sign his checks and business papers with his infamous "X." But that day, Daddy pulled out that piece of paper where I'd written his name and proceeded to copy it onto the back of his check. Standing next to him, I saw that he wrote it big because I had written it big. He copied it just as I had written it with the loop in the J and the awkward-looking Y. It appeared with the same apprehension I felt when he copied the G because I noticed I had written it backwards.

I was to watch Daddy go through this process several times, and then one day, Daddy didn't take the paper from his wallet when he signed the back of his check! He signed his name, turned to me, winked, and said, "Thanks, Baby Girl." That day I was so proud of myself and Daddy.

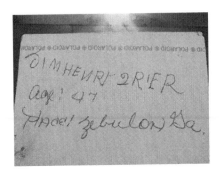

I saw the actual signature on the back of a photo I found five years after I wrote this story.

My Daddy, To Me

I longed for you, Daddy
I needed to cleave unto you every day of my life
But you left me a long time ago
All those times you were angry with your wife

Up the steps of the first Greyhound Bus traveling
north
At the small of my back, you pushed
As if I was the one responsible
For your heart being brutally crushed

You, the first man to ever break my heart
Causing pain that became part of my soul
You let me go when I needed you most
Me being just eleven years old

"It wasn't me, Daddy,"
I'd scream with my arms open wide
Tears streaming through frowns of sorrow
Tears I was no longer able to hide

Your children, six strong
Left totally out of the occasion
Reduced our family to none
After you and Mama's separation

No calls to say you missed me
Asking no questions of how I felt
My only answers came from God
As every night on my knees, I knelt

And prayed that you'd missed me, too
I prayed you'd ease my pain
But at the end of every day, I knew
Separated, we would remain

I cannot give you credit
For strength given me when I needed to endure
The pain I've felt from your rejection
Was soothed only by God,
My Protector and my cure…for sure

To My Captor,
My Husband

A hurt heart doesn't know when it's time to trust, so
it just stops trusting

So, it's important that I say this.

Too much time passed before I realized your
intentions for me
I shouldn't have had to feel the pain coming from
you, but I did
I was so good to you and never understood
How you could ever mistreat me, yet you did

You sat atop my wings when you knew I needed
you beneath them

In my opinion, it shouldn't have been my time
But to you, it was
It should've become clear to you,
But it never did.
Me leaving was the answer,
But you never dreamed I would

And why did I hear things you tried hard not to say?
When I told you how much you had hurt me,
I was the one who suffered when you felt that you
hadn't
So now, if you're hurting, I'm happy that you are!

You! A smooth brotha' in disguise,
Who shared that sparkle in your eyes

With me

I took you up on it
Gave myself up too quick
Only to find later that the hand I was dealt would
leave me taking
Forty years to love myself out of an emotional
wilderness created by you

I devoted all of my love to only you
Someone incapable of being true
You took my treasure I gave for free
Because I loved you to a fault

I 'over-loved' you!
Loved you too much for you to even recognize it as
being love
You sidestepped your responsibility of loving me
back,
With your lack of discipline
To reciprocate with love in kind.
Another woman on your mind!
All the time!

Pseudo-lover!
You thought it not necessary to show me mine,
The way I needed to be loved intentionally
For who I am, and not for your created, made-up
image
Of supposed/ifs/perhaps/maybe me
The Mrs. Saved All My Love for you, 'Me.'

In your selfish way of loving,

You unknowingly preserved me as I laid in wait
For a plan to escape

Hidden in plain sight,
I took flight
In clear view of the darkness exposing your truth,
My heart reflected,
Then in hindsight, disconnected...

And I now face the world as free!
Like *Miss Celie* with the upper hand!
Like *Miss Sophia* out of jail!
I finally broke loose from your captivity,
And I'm still standing!

Capital 'H'-i-m'

When I picture myself in my mind, I see my sistahs
I see us, and we wear faces of sorrow as we cover
Our trapesing after false reciprocities from that
particular lover
And we find ourselves unable to recover
Our lost faith in our own ability to make ourselves
smile
Because we depend on Him to do it

To control you, he views as his best deal
He thrives on variety, and you're His favorite meal
But to you, this does not appeal
That terrible way He makes you feel

You can't even talk Him into treating you better
Not even when you follow to the letter
His plan for you
To always be true...only to Him

Background to his foreground
He set out to lower your high hopes
Set out to change the scope
Of your desire for a better tomorrow

You are His pillar of salt, frozen in time
For there is no season, reason or rhyme
For Him relegating you to the past
While deeming Himself your future

Your misery account is overdrawn...it's overspent
You're being told to relent

You, a broken, unrequited love token
Who's left that relationship smokin' mad
Incredibly sad...

But later encouraged and willing
You put in check, your feelings
And give His love another try

And the cup He bringeth
Though it burns your lips
You take another sip of Him anyway
It burns, but you tell yourself you can handle it

But then the pain becomes a part of you
Manifested in how you keep putting Him
And everyone else ahead of yourself
Because you think that if you don't relent
You, He'll resent
And that it's your fault
For the assault
That He heaps upon your emotions

You just keep sipping from His cup...
It burns...
It just keeps burning...
Each and every time!

Sistahs!
Let's make it easy, like Sunday morning,
And find ourselves something cool to sip!

Truman's Wife

My walk from the university to the Medical Arts Building wasn't too bad. I needed the exercise, as evident by my labored breathing. I felt exhaustion weighing me down as I entered the lobby for my scheduled visit, then walked into the waiting area of Dr. Sheryl Hall's office. *'I need to lose weight. I'm fat and ugly. Friction from my thighs rubbing together ruined yet another pair of hose. My life has become a living hell. Things got too far out of control.'* These are some of the things that ran over and over in my mind, and I couldn't shake it. I take a seat in one of the wooden, plaid blue-and-white chairs that squeaks loudly as I lower myself into it, causing others in the room to raise their heads and look in my direction. I nod politely to everybody as I hurriedly choose to read an issue of <u>Ebony</u>

<u>Magazine</u> with Aretha Franklin on the cover. Flipping through the magazine, I find myself wondering again about my life and how messed up things had gotten.

During my last visit, Dr. Hall said she felt it was important that I pinpoint when I first noticed changes in my husband. I remember telling her it was when Truman said, a few times, that he knew more about the Bible than his teacher. And he decided after many years we weren't going to attend Bible Study any longer. Yet, I sat there shrugging my shoulders because I really didn't know. *I'm not quite sure about anything anymore.*

When Truman and I first met back in 1973, I thought we'd be together forever. He'd told me he was twenty-two years old then, but one of his family members let it leak a few years later that he was actually twenty-nine years old. But I was only sixteen and flattered that such a handsome older guy had even taken time out to speak to me. He asked me if I'd go on a date with him. I accepted, which was our beginning. He wooed me. He pursued me. He swept me off my feet. I fell in love quickly and believed he loved me, too. Back then, we had so much fun together. I'd been abandoned by both my parents on the same day. When Truman entered my life, he added the necessary ingredient I needed to fill many voids. I intended to hold on to him and never live without him.

But now he's gone from me, and it's only been two months since all of my babies survived that terrible accident. Guilt racks my soul, and I keep thinking that there should have been something more I could have said or done to protect my babies! He'd said they were all gonna die! I wish I had taken them

and left home when they were younger! I doubt that

I'd done everything within my power to get Truman

to stop his madness. I pray to God I had.

Hearing, "Excuse me, Miss, Dr. Hall is ready
to see you," pulled me back outside my daydream. I
raised my weary body out of the chair, walked down
the hallway, and took a left turn to get to her office.
Dr. Hall was sitting in her big winged back chair next
to the couch, waiting for me when I entered. She got
up and extended her hand for me to shake, but we
ended up hugging and patting each other on the back.
At our very first session, I'd felt at ease with Dr. Hall.
Standing only four-foot-nine, her presence always
seemed to have a calming effect.

I sat down on the couch and started where I'd
left off at my last session. I began telling her more of

the strange things Truman did over those years before I'd had him committed to a mental health facility. I was also carrying the burden of guilt for making that decision.

"As I was saying," I continued, "something strange had taken over Truman's mind. There was something almost sinister about him when he'd say to our children and me, "There is none like me in the earth, and I'm a perfect, upright man." Yes, that's how he spoke of himself. As "Perfect and upright, and one that fears God." He'd say, "I'm the man, baby! I'm the man!" And I'd sometimes say, 'But Truman, you're not! You're not the man."

Having read the Bible from cover to cover many times with our children as they were growing up, we were both able to recite certain passages verbatim. Many of our friends called Truman to ask where to find this or that in the Bible. He told them, and they would respond with, "Man, how do you remember all that stuff?" Truman started to get a little too full of himself because comments like that made him even more arrogant. His biblical interpretations metastasized into delusions of grandeur. Occasionally, someone would ask my thoughts on a specific subject. I'd always preface my answer with "it's all in the interpretation and who's doing the interpreting." Truman would say, "Ah, she doesn't know what she's talking about." And he hated it when anyone agreed with me. Most times when we had company, the two of us would end up arguing with each other long after everyone had left.

As the months and years passed, even Truman's voice began to sound different. It was like it wasn't *his* voice anymore. He kept saying he was being tested by The Almighty himself and that, "By God, I'm going to do everything in my power to pass His test." Truman would call the children and me into our living room three times a day and demand that we pray a single prayer he had written. That prayer became the only one we recited because Truman would not allow our children's prayers or mine to be uttered. Day after day, I noticed our children become disengaged, and they told me that they were tired of having to "perform" for their father. I told them that they should pray when they were alone because that's what I'd started doing.

Truman's handsomeness started to fade, too. When I'd first met him, he was fine! He was a good-looking man who took great care with his grooming and hygiene. I couldn't believe it when he suddenly stopped shaving. He cited scripture that commanded a man not to shave the corners of his beard, then he decided to grow one. But Truman wore an unkempt, unattractive-looking beard and he absolutely refused to do anything to make it look better.

Truman would say that he "prayed for our children and me, just in case we sinned." He threatened to disavow any vows he'd hear us make to The Almighty. He justified it with 'because as head of this household, I have the power to do so.' He became extreme with his interpretations of a lot of the scriptures we studied. I slept with this man every night and saw him transform into a stranger right before my eyes.

Truman suffered from insomnia and would stay awake reading and studying the scriptures for many consecutive nights. He was 'the man,' but there were many mornings I'd awaken to find him curled up in the fetal position like a baby. One night, Truman asked me to look at a rash of tiny red blisters that started on his scalp and ran along the entire left side of his body, all the way to the bottom of his foot. I *Googled* 'tiny red blisters,' and the information suggested that he might have a case of the Shingles. I told him I'd make him an appointment to see a doctor, but he insisted that I shouldn't, saying, "The Almighty will heal me."

Some nights I'd make him several cups of chamomile tea to drink to try to get him to relax. To appease him, I lied and told him that I understood what he was going through, as I pulled him close and made him lay his head on my lap while I massaged him. It was almost like taking care of a newborn baby whose days and nights are turned around. He'd refused to hold a job only a few months after we'd gotten together, and everything that went wrong in our household, he blamed on "the system." "It's just as well. We don't need to appease the man! I'm a Man of God. Our wealth is gonna be returned sevenfold. You wait and see," he explained.

As far as the scriptures were concerned, I started to doubt my own beliefs. Some days I didn't even know what I believed anymore. But I witnessed Truman struggle against himself when he'd twist the shit out of reality to make it fit the religious fantasy that only he was following after. He struggled against my hopes and dreams, my freedom, and the faith I'd placed in him to get his life together. We argued more and more about scriptures. Ultimately I ended up following his way, even when in my heart I knew he misinterpreted many scriptures that gave him an excuse not to follow them. For Truman, I put my life on hold. I placed it on my broken back burner. My babies often said we were worshipping their father, not The Almighty. Now I see that they were right.

Each day I was becoming more and more resentful towards Truman. As our children grew older, they, too became more resentful and continued to question their father's intentions. They questioned my intentions as well; hell, I questioned my own intentions! I was scared and hadn't realized the detriment Truman's revelations put on our children and me, as we were commanded by him to "separate ourselves from the heathens among our family and friends."

Our four daughters were born in six years. Year after year, as each one turned eighteen, they were eager to emancipate. So, they found their own apartments and moved out of the house. This was bittersweet for me because, sadly, I was left alone to deal with Truman, as he sat at home all day and wouldn't lift a hand to do any work around the house. His appearance continued to spiral downward. The girls stopped dropping by as often because they were upset when they saw their father's appearance and saw me struggle to keep things afloat. He desperately needed to go see a doctor but kept refusing to go. He still wasn't sleeping well, was always on some kind of fast he'd made up for strife and debate, and he started to look gaunt and emaciated. But he would look at our daughters and me and call us fat and tell us we needed to fast more often. He found fault in *everybody* but himself, argued with everybody, said he didn't like anyone, and everyone was jealous of him. At one of our last feast celebrations, Truman told a couple of his friends they "looked feminine" because they still shaved their beards after he'd told them it was a sin to mar the corners of their beards. Family and friends stopped coming by, and told me they were just tired of arguing with him. I hid my deep concerns about Truman from everybody. Mostly, I felt so ashamed for the way he bullied me into doing things his way by reminding me that I was 'just a woman' and needed to 'stay in my place.'

There were only a couple of friends Truman had who didn't stop coming to visit. One evening when they stopped by, Truman told the three of us of a recurring vision he sometimes had when he could sleep. Truman said he kept seeing something terrible happening to our daughters in the vision. And there was nothing anyone could do to stop it because it was part of his test! When I heard him saying that, I tried to reason with Truman. I told him if anything that terrible ever happened to our children, it was because he probably sinned against The Almighty some way, somehow. Both friends nodded their heads in agreement, and I said, "You have lost your mind! How could you say such a thing?" That because of 'your test,' something terrible is going to happen to our children? Really, Truman? He shrugged his shoulders and said, "Woman, you never listen to me. I keep telling you it's not me; it's The Almighty, and this *is* my test."

The very next night, I'd left Truman sleeping in our bedroom. Still, I couldn't fall asleep myself, so I went into the living room and turned on the television, and started watching some local news. Within minutes, "Breaking News" scrolled across the top of the television screen. A reporter explained a terrible accident with possibly four fatalities had occurred on I-75 North near the Glendale/Milford Exit about an hour ago. It involved a black four-door sedan and a semi. I turned up the volume, and the reporter continued with, "The driver of the semi appears to have suffered multiple injuries. It appears that all four passengers in the car were fatally injured."

I felt my heart pounding. My daughters had borrowed my car that night and planned to ride together to a birthday celebration for one of our oldest daughter's friends. They'd taken I-75 North to get there! The news cameras panned over to a huge missing section of guard rail and stopped on a view of the semi. I could see a crumpled dark-colored car almost completely pinned underneath it. Then as

I looked closer, I immediately recognized my black Nissan Altima's license plate, MT L8LY, and knew that it was *my* babies! I felt the hairs on the back of my neck stand up, and huge beads of sweat from my nose and upper lip rolled past my lips and down to my chin and neck. I could taste my fear. My heart ached, and I couldn't breathe as I clutched my chest and screamed and screamed and screamed! That's my car! It's my babies! Oh my God! Truman! It's our babies, and they're in an accident!" I made it into the bedroom and found Truman standing next to the bed, tearing off his clothes. He'd cut his hair as his head was completely bald, and oozing blisters covered the left side of his body from head to toe. It was like watching a horror movie monster, as he dropped down on his knees and started praying his prayer.

I bent down and screamed to him that we needed to go to our babies and that on the news, they had said all the people in the car could be..."Dead," he said. "I know... I know." He was in no condition to go with me. I couldn't stay there with him, and I didn't have time to listen to his whys. I called my friend, Winona, and told her about the accident, asked her to please drive me to the scene, and changed my clothes. She arrived within minutes to drive me to the scene of the accident. As we neared the exit, we saw ambulance and emergency vehicle lights flashing across the interstate. We got out of the car and stopped when we saw the beginning of skid marks where the semi traveling in the middle lane had jack-knifed. About a thousand feet farther away, the trailer part had flipped over onto the top of my car, which was in the far-left lane, and had flattened it like it was a toy.

With thoughts racing, all I knew was that I needed to get to my babies! I broke away from Winona first, then a Police Officer, and took off running towards the accident before another Officer tackled me from behind. In slow motion, as if falling during a dream, my landing seemed soft. I ended up in a puddle of water that saturated my clothing, and I felt blades of grass tickle my lips and nose. Just before I lost consciousness, I heard someone say that they'd heard crying and screaming coming from the car. I felt myself gag as I began to pray. Then there was darkness.

By the time I'd regained consciousness, I saw it was daylight, and I was in a hospital bed. I felt dazed and extremely sore all over. The attending nurse said my getting tackled had caused a couple of bruised ribs, and I'd been in the hospital for a couple of days. I started to remember what happened, and the blood pressure monitor started beeping louder and faster. I screamed, "Where are my babies? Are my babies alright?" She told me that it was a miracle that my babies had all survived. She said they were all out of the ICU and that they were slowly recovering. After hearing this good news, I broke down crying, but these were 'happy' tears. The Almighty had heard my prayer and didn't take my babies away from me. They may be all grown, but they will always be my babies.

I was released from the hospital before noon that same day with a prescription for heavy-duty pain killers. I was also instructed not to be too sedentary, to move around, and be active as much as possible so my ribs would heal. I was able to check in on each of my babies, who were all heavily sedated. I gently touched them, said a silent prayer thanking The Almighty for His grace, then quietly tipped out of their rooms.

Winona had been in the hospital waiting room all night and the next day waiting to hear about my babies and me. When she saw me, she gently embraced me and let me know how worried she'd been. She said several people had sent get well wishes and prayers for my children and me. Still, everyone was also very worried about Truman and how seemingly uncaring he appeared to be about the danger we'd just gone through.

When I arrived home, I immediately looked for Truman inside the house but couldn't find him. As I walked past the kitchen window that faced the backyard, I saw him outside sitting on the ground. Apparently, he had started a fire in the iron basin close to where he sat, as heavy, dark smoke billowed up towards the cloud-filled sky. Truman stood up, then poured the ashes he'd taken from the basin onto his head, completely covering himself. He slowly fell to his knees, and I saw his shoulders slump. I rushed out of the house and ran down to where he knelt. Inside the slippers he wore, I could see Truman's feet were completely crusted over with ooze from blisters, and had also stuck to his clothes when he'd covered himself with ashes.

I could not believe what I was seeing! Truman, sitting in a pile of ashes in the middle of our backyard, chanting, standing, kneeling, and praying his prayer. I ran to him, kneeled down, getting as close as possible, and asked him what he was doing.

Then I shouted at him to get his behind out of the ashes! I was screaming at him that all of our babies had almost died! I kept asking him if he'd heard what I was saying. All of our babies could have died! Then as I raised myself up, I could see our neighbor, Mr. Neal peering through his screened-in porch. Then I heard him threaten, "I'll call 911, if that fool doesn't stop his nonsense." I kept trying to grab Truman's arm, but he kept pulling away. I kept begging him to please come inside the house. Mr. Pierce, our neighbor who lived directly across the street, was taking his daily walk. As he walked past our house he called out, "You know that insurance won't pay off if you commit suicide!"

Again I knelt down, and got as close to Truman as I possibly could, and I cupped his ash-covered, tear-streaked face in my hands. He shook his head slightly, turned, and looked at me with a blank stare. Then I looked deep into his eyes and tried to connect with something inside him, but I saw...nothing! I felt like Truman was no longer there! My man is gone; it was as if his soul had been snatched away. Any reality holding him here had been sucked up inside the dark hovering smoke cloud that sat directly above us. I only saw emptiness in his eyes. He didn't even recognize me. That scared the shit out of me as I realized I had completely lost him. I didn't have a clue how I would ever be able to explain to anybody just what really happened."

Finally, I summed it up for Dr. Hall, "My man is gone away from me. But my babies are all alive! He had said our babies would perish so that he could maintain his perfection and pass his test! Perfection for what? For his life only? For his human-ness only? How can anyone have a goal only for himself if he's got a wife and children? What about his children's perfections? What about my perfection? Don't we count? I begged him to stop! I kept telling him he was taking it too far! My babies are my purpose now, and I have to do this alone. But, until The Almighty sees fit, I'll have to go on living with guilt until I'm released, and I will lean into my own faith until I am."

I Am of Job's Wife

Would it be too big of a stretch if I claim to be in the lineage of the ancestry of Job's wife? What's going to happen to me if I put claims on it?

I ask because daily I've experienced pain akin to the pain Job's wife must have felt as she watched her existence end. We are led to believe that when she told Job to "Curse God and die," it placed her among those viewed unfavorably. But *I am* of Job's wife. But, please don't view me unfavorably because I swallow guilt, because I overindulged in pain and sorrow as I watched my children's pain and sorrow while being led unawares to the role they played in their father's suffering. Suffering that he never viewed as suffering. I was forced to ignore my own agony because I had no say in the matter. Like Job's wife, I was forced to question my man's sanity.

Especially when my husband began to express prophetic beliefs about himself and his claim of being the only one who wholly served The Almighty no matter the consequence, under any and all circumstances. Daily I wept for him and my children, who were never returned to *'us,'* as they struggled through their own realities. I saw *something in them die* when they, too, witnessed their father's suffering that eventually took hold and consumed him.

I watched my husband change right before my eyes. It was terrifying to witness a daily transformation of his reality as he slipped deeper and deeper into beliefs that eventually altered his physical appearance. The unreasonable beliefs he expressed about my role as his wife brought into question my love for him over and over. His beliefs intoxicated my thoughts with fear of what would happen if I ever spoke of my own feelings. But I was there, too. I witnessed it in panoramic view, and it messed me up! I walked away damaged. My cries of pain were seemingly ignored. I suffered through not being able to reason with my husband any longer. When I ceased to speak, and he slipped completely from my embrace. I couldn't escape reality because it was smacking me dead in the face. Hearing our babies' cries of "What's wrong with him?" Cries of them asking, "Why is this happening to us," were heard again and again. Cries drowned out only by my muffled cry of, "Please help me, My Father." Cries that were exonerated because, in the end, I was allowed to live to tell my story.

Withered

I stood and watched four slices of bacon in a cast-iron skillet slowly wither into a puddle of fat.

I stood there thinking that this process parallels the anxiety I've felt draining off of my soul...
Dehydrating my joy.

The weariness of my soul stares back at me in the mirror.

Why?

Because I am the bacon in the skillet, and the heat is on!
I am the bacon in the skillet; listen to my song.
I am the bacon in the skillet; somebody prove me wrong.

Cursed am I as I live on the outer edges of blessings.
Uncertain of how or what I need to do to infiltrate happiness.
To transfuse joy inside the tube that feeds me life.

Feeling consumed by hard times and fearing failure … again, as I pray for a breakthrough in my search for peace of mind.
As I pray for assurance that hurting pain will go...

And stay
Away
Continuing to wonder why pain is all I gain,
And I'm getting on my own nerves trying not to get
on anyone else's.

Why?

Because I am the bacon in the skillet, and the heat is
on!
I am the bacon in the skillet; listen to my song.
I am the bacon in the skillet, but SOMEBODY
finally proved me wrong!

If You Are My Man …
And I Am Your Whoa-man

If you are my man,
And I am your whoa-man,
This is the purpose of my creation...
You will walk away from me every single time
knowing real love
As we are missing links who've found each other
Coupling to become saturated in pleasure
Where there is no measure
That compares to the treasure
I have for you here

My passion will raise you up
And prepare you to get laid
Unafraid
To reach your hardest goal
Then lose control
Trying hard...not to

My passion is always on reserve in your name
Our paths cross perfectly through, then into each
other
Creating thoughts that make us shudder
You discover my depth
As you probe for deeper satisfaction

Then we…
Pulse/Glide
Pulse/Glide
Pulse/Glide

Unable to disguise
Your most prized
Erection's
Delivery of affection

Your saxophone explodes
Inside my love
I feel the rhythmic beating of your heart
Urgently spread my legs apart
Ready to inspire
'Your' desire
I give 'you' butterflies

You are my Pound Cake
I am your "Any Flavor You Want" Ice Cream
We taste good to each other
You excite my 'secret' spot
And do all the things that keep me...hot!
Because, 'you' are the one

Daydreaming keeps you up at night
Even when I'm nowhere in sight
You feel me touching
Your standing at attention presence

We cry out!
We understand!
You are my man!
And I am your whoa-man!
And know for surety
You'll never give me a chance
To ever stop loving you!

Where I Belong

Actions I needed to take
For my own sake
Made me see what was at stake
When I faked
Happiness

The fog in my mind has lifted
Through webs of deceit, I've sifted
I now realize that I'm gifted
And it started at birth …
Else I wouldn't be here

You can't stifle my fame
So, stop slandering my name
You see me, I'm real
No matter how 'you' may feel

I remain claimed by those who care
Those not going anywhere
Unless I, too, am there

Feeling protected
Not neglected
Feeling spiritually perfected

In tune from the womb
Here I stand
Not a minute too soon!

Take It the Way 'You' Need To

We arrive fresh in this world with a love for 'something.' Something that keeps us going...living and learning to move towards 'it.' That force of divine order calls your name, and you answer.

A territorial creature longing to belong. A damaged good with a refined soul...A renewed spirit who's allowed to live another day. You are. I am. Allowed to transition from suffering. To spring forth from harsh realities.

Expecting to be treated royally in every aspect of living the life for which we have been chosen. Allowed to survive because that 'something' greater than you favors you. Seeing to it that the will set forth is accomplished in time...at the right time. As the Earth goes about its business of fulfilling a commandment of replenishing with goodness, we are encouraged to arise and bear witness and know that the road laid out before us will take us where we need to be...in order to exist.

Tears are wiped away after yet another episode, as we try to make meaning of our blessings while living through a promised curse.

An awareness of the limits of what can be controlled by you, stirs up a feeling inside as you look into your children's eyes and see a mirror image of you reflecting in your mother's eyes...in your father's eyes...

See joy? Sometimes you f-e-e-l joy …
See hurt? Sometimes you f-e-e-l hurt …

Connecting events to unknowns, to unawares.
Remembering to one day ask, "Well damn, why do
I act like that?" Some good things, some bad things
happened on sunny Sunday afternoons, drunken
Friday nights, and stormy Mondays that made you
who you are.

> That gal over there, just like her Mama
> That boy over there, just like his Daddy
> That gal over there, just like her Daddy
> That boy over there, just like his Mama

And you find yourself again in a place where that
'something greater than you' has dropped you off to
represent! It's your time to shine... It's your chance
to fly!

So, acknowledge your perfection...your direct
connection...accept your greatness...live blessed...
be your authentic self. Have a love affair with life!
Embrace your resilience! Stop lyin' to yourself!
Re-claim your legacy!

Letter to Altar'd State

October 13, 2015

Dear Madam/Sir:

A few weeks back, while on my lunch break I walked past your store, Altar'd State, located on Calhoun Street in Cincinnati, OH. Calhoun Street runs parallel to a section of the University of Cincinnati where I'm employed.

I noticed your window displays of cotton stalks and poufs of cotton protruding from burlap bundles as I walked past. I stopped in mid-stride and found myself just standing in front of your plate glass window staring. Transfixed, I was taken back fifty years! I was taken back to my memory of picking cotton and the sad times it represented for me, yet I felt a strong desire to smell that cotton. I wanted to touch it.

I pulled myself away from the display and walked inside the store. I approached the counter where two of your Sales Associates were standing. Smiling, I inquired whether or not I could touch, smell, and maybe even purchase some of the cotton. Years ago, I'd only been paid two cents a pound to pick it. With raised eyebrows, they told me I would have to wait until the displays were broken down before they would be able to let me purchase some of it. I said that I understood, but as I turned to leave, I saw stalks of cotton in a beautiful blue vase on a table across from the counter, so I asked if I could please touch it. Again, with eyebrows raised, they both said, 'sure.'

My desire to touch cotton, under different circumstances in my life, was what I wanted to experience. So, I walked up to the stalks of cotton in the blue vase and I sniffed, then touched the bulbs of cotton. I explained to your Sales Associates that I once picked cotton and how much I hated it when I had to do it. Now, at that precise moment, I was able to see the beauty of the cotton. I explained to them that I was feeling a shift in what cotton represented to me. *(I could tell they didn't have a clue as to what I was talking about, so I kept explaining.)* You see, to touch the cotton again, and this time because I WANTED TO, made me smile hard because now it represents the overcoming of things I'd experienced in my lifetime. It was a beautiful thing to be able to look back at the times when I had to pick cotton, when I had to go to bed hungry, sometimes wake up in the night angry for being hungry, and to now be able to see it and smile. Trust me. As I stood there looking at that cotton, I felt a shift, an urgency to take a certain turn in my journey.

That day made me reassess my freedoms and made me feel damned special, as I looked backward then forward to my present space. Ancestral energy was breathing life back into my familial legacy. It would no longer be unkept. I am assigned to be its keeper until the time returns when we are allowed to enjoy things in life that measure up to things enjoyed in our lives when our ancestors were queens and kings.

Carol's First Taste of Integration

Artistically cut through Georgia's red dirt, graveled roads lined by cotton fields connected the city section of Zebulon to endless acres of farmland, and separated Colored Town from its more affluent sections. This neighborhood was deemed Colored Town during the early 1900s because it was a place where only colored people lived and owned businesses. Miss Emma Lou's Place was the popular spot. Folks would gather to listen to rhythm and blues from 45 rpm vinyl records played on a bright blue jukebox illuminating the dark, dank corner of the establishment. It was a place where one could hang out, buy a soda pop, a bag of pork rinds, play on the pinball machine, or play five records on the jukebox, all for a dollar.

It was late summer 1968. It was a time when segregation was the norm, and the Civil Rights Movement was making slow but steady progress as it forged its way through many small southern towns like Zebulon. On any given day, Monday through Saturday, you'd find Carol and her family, along with several other families, in one of the cotton fields trudging through, planting or picking endless rows of cotton. Sometimes during the late afternoon, as the sun beamed deliberately above uncovered heads, you'd hear a picker in the field shout that civil rights leaders were going to be on the 6:00 o'clock evening news. They would be talking about boycotting businesses, integrating schools, and how colored children deserved to start out on a more even playing field, "Cause this one here sho' ain't even!" Everybody laughed, but it wasn't funny to Carol as she dragged the burlap sack holding the cotton she'd begrudgingly picked. Once home from the fields, children and adults alike crowded around black-and-white television sets. This was a time to watch news reports of peaceful demonstrations, and Coloreds/Negroes, who wrestled with racial identity, demanded their equal rights. It was a time when James Brown belted out the song lyrics, "Say it Loud! I'm Black, and I'm Proud." Music from singer Curtis Mayfield and 60s group, The Impressions, invited those almost ready to give up to 'keep on pushing' and encouraged people 'to get ready, cause the freedom train was coming.'

Carol, an eleven-year-old eighth grader, was intrigued by it all and hung on to every word. She was smart, mature for her age, and curious about the possibility of integration ever occurring in Zebulon.

"Daddy, Mama, they want us to go to school with White kids," she'd ask. "I wanna go! I wanna go! Can I go, please can I go?" Carol wanted to enter the doors of the *White school* she had to pass by each day to get to her own school. She wanted to see what it felt like to be equal to White children. She wanted to stop having to sneak a drink from the *Whites-only* water fountain in the courthouse, and she wanted to enter the *Tea Room Café* through the front door.

Carol was the youngest of six, two boys and four girls. She was born to a mother who had only completed sixth grade and a father who had never attended school. Although his job paid a decent salary for drilling water wells, he didn't contribute to the household. Raising six children was not easy to do on the money Carol's mother was able to bring in.

She had hoped and prayed that all her children would at least be able to graduate from high school.

One of Carol's earliest memories was waking up and being surrounded by a soft, puffy whiteness and not seeing anything beyond the cotton fields. When only her mother was in the fields, those were the times when her brothers and sisters were in school. Carol recalled always longing to attend school, too. When she was just four years old, Mrs. Gates, Carol's younger sister's second-grade teacher, agreed to let her sit in the classroom. This gave her mother an opportunity to work at the local cannery. Soon Mrs. Gates was able to give Carol the same assignments as the second graders and marveled at how quickly she caught on. However, the months of mid-March through June was cotton planting season. Carol's father would hire out his family to local farmers and pull his children out of school to help in the fields. He would show up at school, walk into his children's classrooms, tell the teachers his children were going with him, point his children out, and lead them all out of the building. Carol would slump down as far as she could in her desk. She was embarrassed to see and hear the other students snicker and point at her, but she would obediently follow her father outside. Shamefully, Carol hopped onto the back of her father's old rusted, red pick-up truck and headed to the fields. Carol loved going to school and was always eager to learn something new. But she hated the unnecessary interruption in her learning that the cotton fields forced on her. She would sometimes feign a headache, so she wouldn't have to go.

Carol's family would sometimes attend Mount Hope Baptist Church, located in Colored Town, right next door to Miss Emma Lou's Place. In past weeks, the Reverend had spoken to the congregation about meetings he had with civil rights leaders in Atlanta, Georgia, located 65 miles northwest of Zebulon. The Reverend had expressed to the civil rights leaders a need for their help to end segregation in Zebulon. One particular Sunday, renowned civil rights leader, Reverend Jesse Jackson, who worked in Martin Luther King, Jr.'s Southern Christian Leadership Conference, was the invited guest speaker. Lots of folks had seen Reverend Jackson alongside Dr. Martin Luther King, Jr. on television before Dr. King's untimely assassination on April 4, 1968. To see him in person was one of the most exciting things to happen for Negroes in Zebulon.

Reverend Jackson approached the podium. His left hand lifted the microphone; his right hand made a fist as he raised it high above his head. Then Reverend Jackson started his speech with, "I am! Somebody! I am! Somebody! Soul Power! Soul Power," just as the crowd saw him do on television. The congregation went wild! So moved by his speech, they stood and raised their right hands and made fists. Carol, profoundly affected, stood up, raised her right hand and made a fist too. Along with everyone else, she pledged to participate in this God-inspired fight for the integration of schools, for the freedom to use that *Whites Only* water fountain in the courthouse, and to be able to use the front entrance to the *Tea Room Café*. The church erupted with shouts of "I am! Somebody! I am! Somebody."

Carol was hooked! She was experiencing some self-pride for the first time in her life. That moment was the impetus of her journey to fight against racial discrimination and all forms of social inequality.

Reverend Jackson continued his speech by saying that "there is power in numbers." So, that day, he urged everyone in the church to participate in a freedom march. He wanted to schedule it for the following Tuesday morning. Reverend Jackson asked that all Black teachers, administrators, and children in Zebulon participate in the march by walking out of their schools at 10:00 am. He also asked that they picket outside the local cannery for more decent wages and boycott the *Tea Room Cafe* "until you're allowed to enter through the front door." They were instructed to leave classrooms in single file lines, head to the main entrances of perspective schools, and walk out. Reverend Jackson asked if he could count on everyone there that day. "Yeah!" "You sure can." "I'll be there," and "You can count on me" echoed throughout the church.

As planned, the following Tuesday morning at 10:00, Black teachers, administrators, and children in grades 1-8 at East Pike Elementary, just outside Colored Town, did as instructed and walked out of the school. They marched to Mount Hope Baptist Church, where school buses waited for them. The children loaded onto the buses and were driven to Concord High School, grades 9-12, seven miles away in Concord. The older children had also walked out, and this was where the freedom march was to start. Lined up five to each row, with about 50 rows, this sign of unity had brought together the most people Carol had ever seen in one place in Zebulon.

With several freedom fighters sporting Afro hairstyles that were impeccably groomed, and wearing beautiful African print dashikis, teachers and administrators joined them in the front rows. With schoolchildren carrying signs and singing freedom songs, the march to the courthouse began on that hot, hot day in April, 1969. At the three-mile mark, a few parents had parked alongside the road with coolers in their cars filled with water, Kool-Aid, and bologna sandwiches to give to the marchers. Time seemed to pass quickly because before too long, the marchers could see the courthouse in the near distance. They started to sing, *We Shall Overcome*, louder and louder as they came closer. Reverend Jackson, Dr. Abernathy, several parents, teachers, and school administrators were waiting for the marchers on the front lawn of the courthouse. As they came closer, Reverend Jackson shouted, "I am! Somebody! I am! Somebody!" Everyone joined in with their own shouts. Reverend Jackson quieted the crowd, led the group in a prayer, and congratulated everyone for their help conducting a successful march.

It was necessary for several shorter freedom marches, picketing, and boycotts to take place in Zebulon in order to get the disenfranchised heard. During those peaceful marches, Whites threatened protesters with what would happen to them if they continued marching and boycotting. They were sprayed with fire hoses, dispersed with tear gas, and suffered injury from rocks thrown at them. Carol was among a few, who were mostly children, that the

Sheriff wanted to put fear into by forcing them to spend a night in jail.

Within four months, schools in Zebulon, Georgia, were finally integrated. The *Whites Only* sign had been taken down from above the water fountain in the courthouse, workers had returned to the cannery, but the *Tea Room Café* remained segregated. Carol's chance to go to school with White children was imminent, and she couldn't wait for the first day of school to come for her to *be judged not by the color of her skin but by the content of her character.*

Carol was so excited on her first day in ninth grade. It was her first day in an integrated school. But as her still-segregated school bus arrived at Concord High School, she noticed the White children were getting off buses parked on the opposite side of the schoolyard. She readied herself to exit her bus, and as she stepped off the last step, a tall White man wearing a navy-blue jacket standing outside the door of the bus said, "Children, children, please go inside at this entrance." He pointed to the back entrance of the school while White children scurried into the school through the front entrance. Carol whispered to her friend, Vera, "Wonder why they doin' that," as they walked towards the back entrance. Vera said, "Humph. I don't know, but I don't like it." Carol replied, "Me either."

The Black children entered the school through the backdoor as instructed and then walked into a large auditorium. Carol noticed that only Negro children were there, and at a long table in front of the stage sat four White men and two White women, all wearing navy-blue jackets. There was a sign in the middle of the table that said, "Homeroom Assignments." Carol and Vera eagerly approached one of the women and were happy to see Room 132 was the homeroom for both. They left the auditorium, took a left as directed, and followed the hallway towards Room 132. As they walked past Rooms 126, 128, and 130, they eyed each other curiously when they saw a tall White man wearing a navy-blue jacket in the doorways directing the White children to sit in any seat in the front rows. However, they directed the Black children to sit in the last two rows in the back of the classroom. At East Pike Elementary, Carol had always chosen to sit in the front row. So she decided she had to let the man standing in the doorway of Room 132 know she preferred to sit in the front row. "Come on, Vera. Let's tell him that we want to sit next to each other in the front row." Carol walked up to the man and said, "Excuse me, sir. My name is Carol Grier. My friend, Vera, and I would like to sit in these two seats," pointing to two unoccupied seats in the front row.

The man looked down, then leaned in so close to Carol that she could feel his hot breath spread across her face; and she could see huge blue veins bulging out on both sides of his neck. The smell of stale coffee, garlic, and cigarettes filled her nostrils, her stomach twisted into a knot, and she felt her heart pounding. Vera stood in one spot shaking too, and didn't seem to be able to move. Through clenched teeth, the man said to Carol, "I know who you are. You one of Jim Grier's gals, and if you don't take your little black ass to the back of the room like you 'spose to, you gon' wish you had."

Carol had never felt so scared in all her life!

Not even the time when she got caught trying to steal

bubble gum from Mr. Wade's Grocery Store, and

Mr. Wade promised to tell her daddy. She steadied

herself, turned quickly like a soldier, and headed

towards the back of the classroom. Carol quickly

passed Vera, grabbed her hand, and pulled her along

too. They sat in the last two seats in the far corner of

the last row. With hearts pounding, the knowledge

of defeat, and the inability to force back tears, they

dropped their heads in unison.

Personal Note:
This story is a fact based work of fiction. However, my younger brother was a senior at Concord High School in April, 1969, the time we walked out to protest against segregation in Pike County Schools. Sadly, the fact is that it took the Pike County Board of Education forty-nine (49) years to issue diplomas to the Black seniors who had participated in the walkout.

About the Author

Amuna YisraEL AKA Carol Joyce Grier, the youngest of two brothers and three sisters, was born in Griffin, GA and raised for the first eleven years of her life in Zebulon, GA. Introduced to poetry by her first reading teacher, Amuna tried her hand at writing poetry, prose, and short stories early in her life. As a young girl she composed personal letters for her parents and the elderly in her neighborhood. She participated in, and won her first poetry reading competition at age nine. As an adult, Amuna lasted through to the final round of the 2019 Findlay Market Poetry Slam Competition. For the past few years, Amuna has participated in Writing Circles at Women Writing for (a) Change where they were instrumental in helping her find her voice and hone her writing skills. In 2021, Amuna formed Dream Manifested Company, where she showcases her spoken word talents. She earned a Bachelor's Degree in Organizational Leadership from the University of Cincinnati, where she was employed for many years until she left to pursue her writing endeavors. She's always dreamed of living the life of a writer, and feels that being able to express herself through writing is a gift. Amuna has lived most of her life in Cincinnati, OH, and has four daughters, two sons, and eleven grandchildren.

Contact Information
Amuna YisraEL
Dream Manifested Company
2402 Vienna Woods Drive
Cincinnati, OH. 45211-2904
ayisraey@gmail.com
513-379-3679